D1479489

UNIV. OF MOUNT UNION
CURRICULUM CENTER

SYMBIOSIS

To Ariane

SYM

BIOSIS

A BOOK OF UNUSUAL FRIENDSHIPS

by Jose Aruego

Charles Scribner's Sons / New York

Symbiosis means that two completely different kinds
of animals become close friends in order to help each other.
Often they depend upon one another for survival.
Here are nine of these unusual friendships.

Blue Butterfly
& Ants

When ants find the helpless larva of a blue butterfly, they happily carry it to their nest. They gently rub its back with their antennae so the larva will make sweet drops of honeydew, which the ants love to sip.

The ants feed and protect their fat, wormlike friend until it changes into a beautiful blue butterfly and flies away.

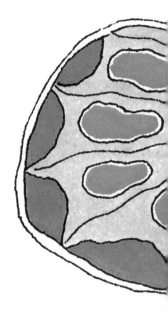

Crocodile & Plover

The ferocious crocodile snaps at anything within reach. And yet he opens his mouth wide to let one kind of bird, the plover, walk in and out. The plover eats leeches and whatever else it finds to pick from between the crocodile's teeth.

As a result of their friendship, the crocodile has clean,
sparkling teeth and the plover has a full tummy.

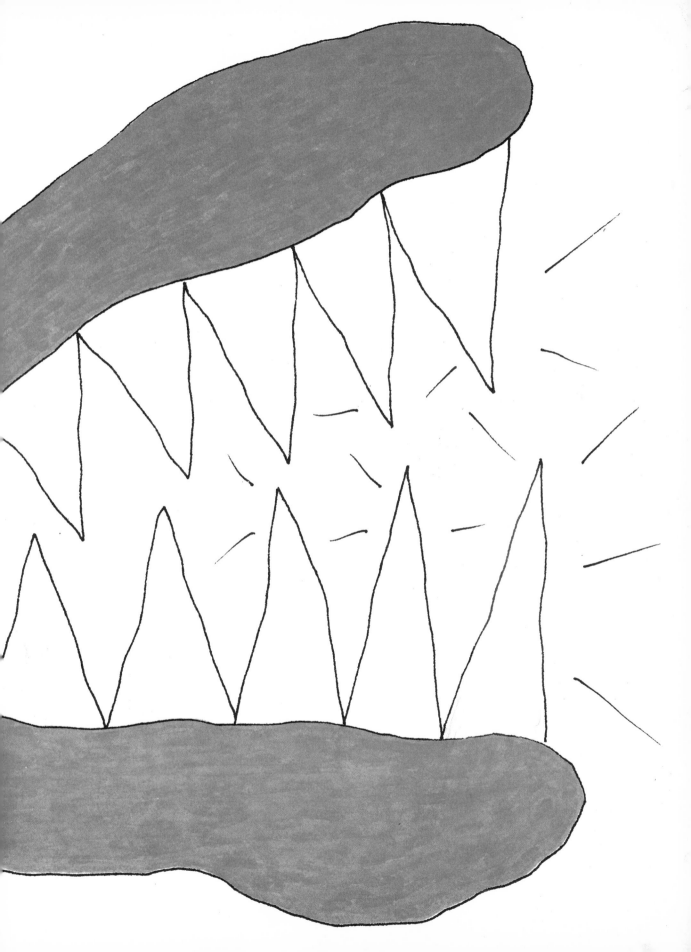

Ostrich & Zebra

The ostrich has very good eyesight, while the zebra has extremely keen hearing. For safety, they often herd together so they can warn each other when prowling lions are near.

Goatfish & Wrasse

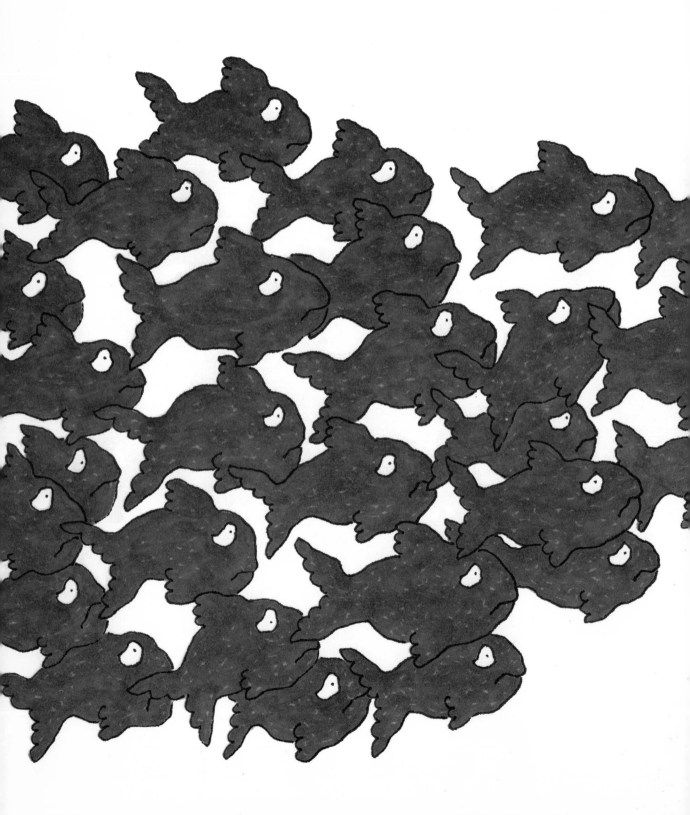

All fish have to be cleaned once in a while to get rid of things caught in their gills. Also, the fungus and bacteria growing on their fins, scales, and in small cuts, can make them sick. So when they are dirty, like these goatfish, they look for the tiny wrasse.

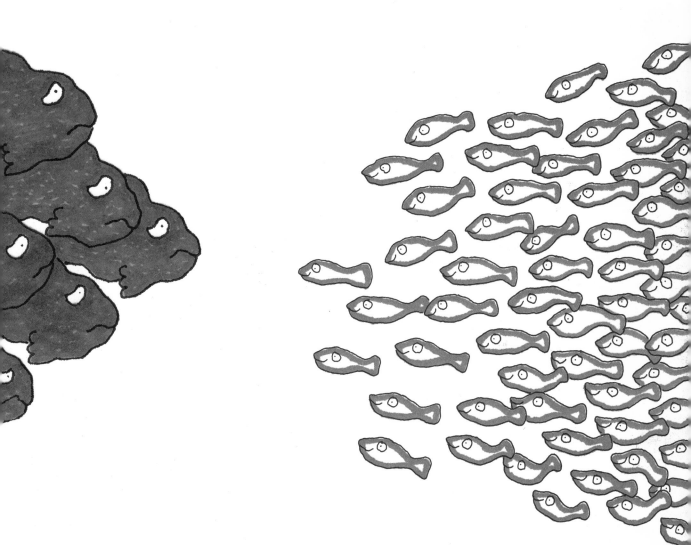

The wrasse carefully nibble away all the clinging parasites on the big fish. And because the large fish will need to be cleaned again, they never swallow up the well-fed wrasse.

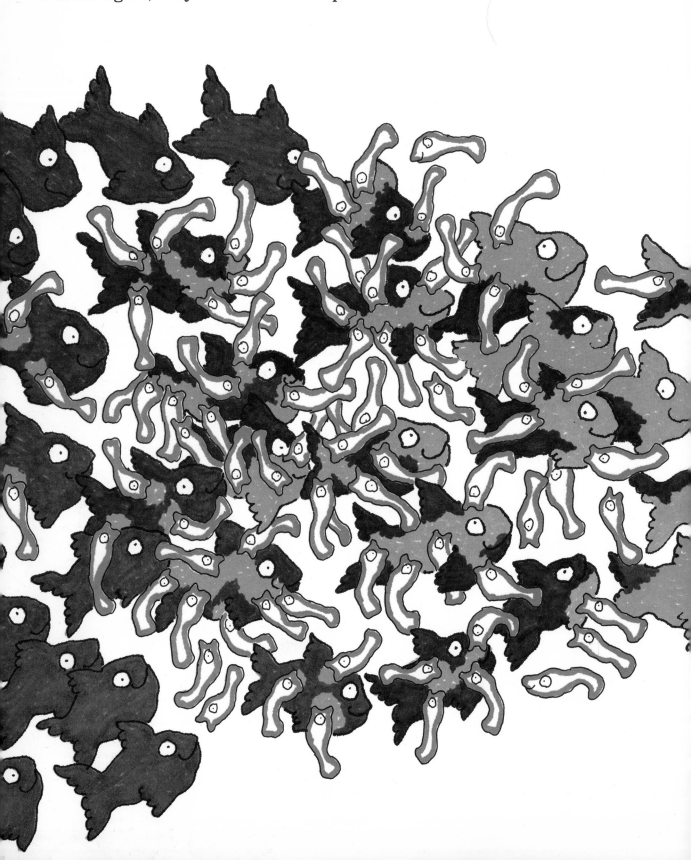

Honey-Guide Bird & Ratel

The African honey-guide loves beeswax. It can easily find a hive but cannot break it open. So this little bird looks for the badger-like ratel, chirps and chatters to get its attention, and leads it to the hive. The ratel grunts to let the bird know he is following.

Upon reaching the beehive, the ratel immediately leaps on it, tears it apart with his claws and greedily devours the honey. The infuriated bees try to sting the ratel, but he doesn't care, for his thick fur and tough skin protect him.

After the ratel has licked up all the honey, he happily trots off, still surrounded by the swarm of angry bees. When everyone is gone, the honey-guide is finally able to get at the honeycomb and enjoy his favorite meal.

Sooty Shearwater & Tuatara

The tuatara is too lazy to build his own home. He waits around
all night catching bugs while the sooty shearwater bird sleeps
in the burrow she has dug for herself.

As soon as the sooty shearwater leaves her burrow to hunt for fish each day, the sleepy tuatara crawls into the nest. To repay the bird for her hospitality, the tuatara rids their home of centipedes, beetles, and flies.

Man-of-War & Nomeus Fish

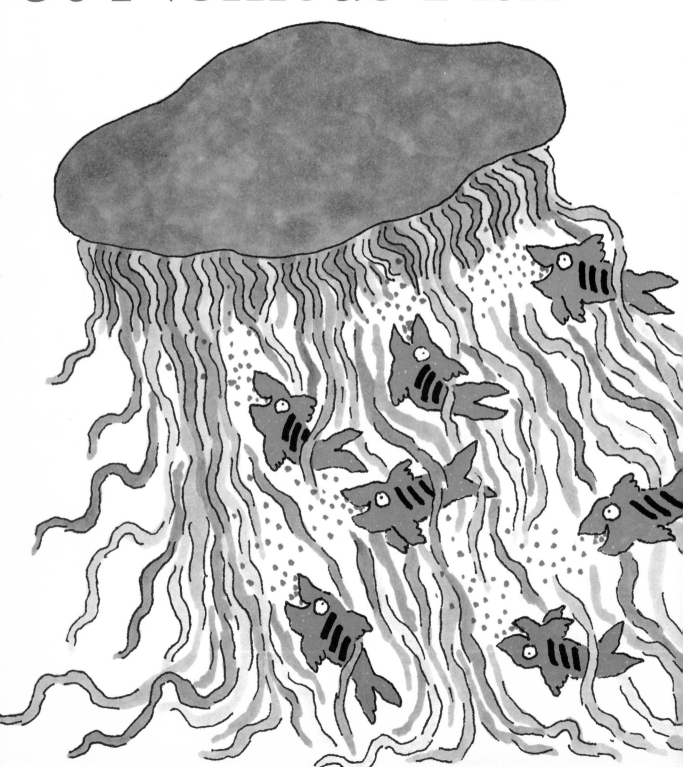

The Portuguese man-of-war is a fearful creature. It stings and paralyzes fish with its long dangling tentacles. Only the nomeus fish is unharmed by its sting. In fact these fish like the man-of-war so well that they live among the tentacles and bring food to share with their host.

When chased by larger fish, the nomeus quickly retreats
to the safety of the stinging tentacles.

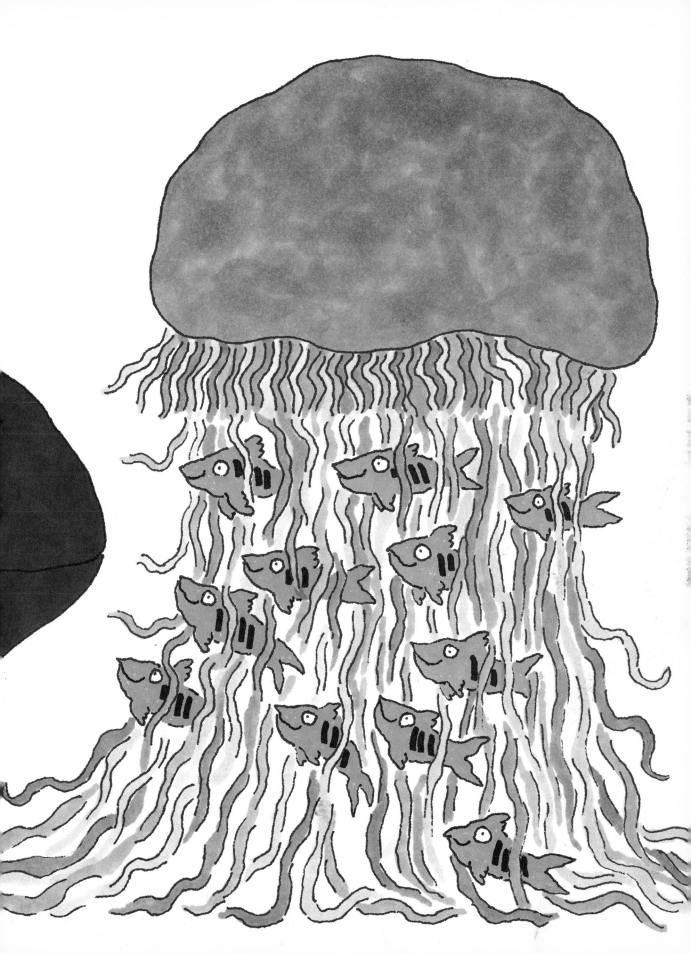

Rhinoceros & Cattle Egret

The rhino is delighted and relieved to have the cattle egret as his constant companion. The egret eats all the itching, biting bugs off the rhino's back and considers them a delicious meal.

The egret also sounds the alarm if anybody is silly enough
to try to sneak up on them while the rhino is sleeping.

Lybia Crab & Sea Anemones

Before going into dangerous places, the Lybia crab picks up small sea anemones in its front claws to defend itself against enemies wishing to gobble him up. Armed with the stinging anemones, the crab is quite safe from even his largest and most fearsome foes.

Sea anemones are unable to move about by themselves and always welcome a ride to a new feeding place.